D0612905

10

MINUTE
BOOT CAMP

FOR YOUR BRAIN

Publisher: Simon Melhuish
Managing Editor: Nikole G Bamford
Puzzle Compiler: Fran Pickering
Designer: Linley Clode
Contributing Designer: Sarah Wells

Designed and compiled by
The Lagoon Group
PO Box 311, KT2 5QW, UK
PO Box 990915, Boston, MA 02199, USA

ISBN: 978-1-1906170-69-1

www.thelagoongroup.com

Printed in China

EcoPrint is the planet friendly imprint of The Lagoon Group, where extra care is taken to be eco friendly.

 FSC Certified – These books are printed in conjunction with FSC certified materials. By using FSC certified materials we can guarantee that the paper used comes from well-managed forests.

 Footprint initiative – We all want to protect and preserve our environment, so let's try to reduce our carbon footprint one day at time.

 Re-use – Book Recycling Schemes: we actively support book recycling schemes that exist to redistribute used books. See www.bookcrossing.com for an international scheme.

 Don't despair: you can share! – Pass this book on to friends, neighbours, strangers! Every book that is re-read is one less book that needs to be printed.

 Book swap – Look for a book swap scheme in your area – or start your own! It's a great way to enjoy different books and reduce their impact on the environment.

 Do your bit for charity – Why not donate your unwanted books to charity. You'll be bringing a smile to someone less fortunate AND protecting the environment!

 Don't forget to look at home and work or just about anywhere to see what you can...**Recycle, recycle, recycle!**

H W L L L L

Can you work out the phrase?

Rearrange the 11 matches
to make nine.

3

Last week I had a visit
from a friend who told
me that each night
she wakes up and gets out
of bed at least 180 times.
Yet she always sleeps for
at least 7 hours at a time.

How can that be?

4

FAREDCE

Can you work out the phrase?

5

a) **SPILL CATCHER**

b) **GLANCE**

c) **TRACKER**

The answer to these clues
are palindromes.

Which butterfly is the odd one out?

7

a) STONE. WOOD. FORM.

b) WRIST. POCKET. OBSERVE.

c) FROZEN. VINSON. PENGUIN.

Using the clues provided,
can you find the objects?

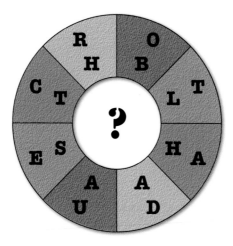

8

Place a letter in the center
of the circle so that four
five-letter words can be rearranged
from each straight line of letters.

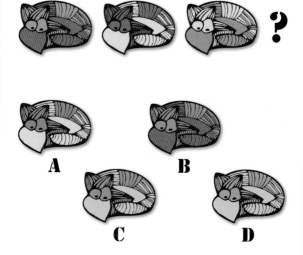

Which creature completes
the sequence?

END

JUMPING

CLOSURE

What phrase is represented here?

John's uncle phoned him to wish him Happy Birthday. John said 'The day before yesterday I was 12 and next year I will be 15!'

How can that be?

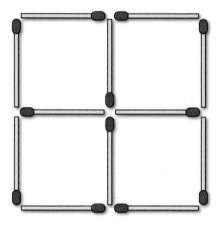

Rearrange two matches to
make seven squares.

13

EXA		ATE
KIT		AKE
FEN		EEK
WIN		ASS
TRE		OUS
SLI		ACK
REC		ENT
PRI		ESS
CRO		IRE
ANI		ITY

SSF	MUL	UGR	RCH	MAL
IPI	TIW	NGB	EGL	EST

Complete the words in the grid by
filling each space with a group of
three letters from the list.

a) HELIUM. MEASURE. FLOAT.

b) SING. SNAILS. SPECKLES.

c) RED. PH. VINEGAR.

Using the clues provided, can you
find the word in each case?

15

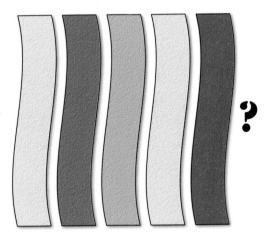

?

What comes next in the
sequence above?

```
D A O M E E O G E N
S I N I N P L A H U
I D I O L O C H S C
E A S E B A I N S K
T E I L U T V E L A
S S N O C L U N O M
U E D I T E Y L R B
R S C A I S M A T A
E P M P C Y L S P S
W O E E I R I A O T
```

If you find the correct
starting letter you should be able
to read 17 words through the maze.
The last letter of each word
becomes the first of the next.

17

The zoo is flooded.
The keeper needs to get the
lion, the antelope and the
chimp by boat to higher
ground on an unflooded island.
However, his boat has only
room for one animal but he
cannot leave the antelope
alone with either the lion
of the chimp. How will he
get all three to safety?

333

37

111

222

What is the connection
between these numbers?

What phrase is represented here?

Using four straight lines within the sun's orb, how many sections can you divide it into? They do not have to be equal in area.

21

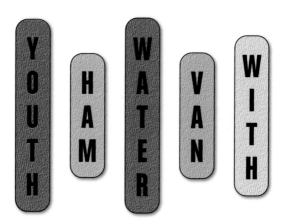

Which word is the odd one out?

ROADSTER

Take away one letter at a time to
leave a complete word each time.

It was time for the
annual strongman contest.
The four finalists were Boris,
Basil, Bertram and Boyd.

Boyd and Boris together proved
stronger than Basil and Bertram.

Basil and Boris were a stronger
team than Bertram and Boyd.

Basil on his own was stronger
than Boris and Bertram.

Can you list the order in
which the four finalists were
graded, strongest first?

Can you divide this square
into five sections, all equal
in size and shape?

You have two buckets.
One holds exactly
5 liters and the other
exactly 7 liters.
How will you transfer
exactly 9 liters
from a pond to
a fish tank?

KER		ONE
WIT		ISM
THE		TIC
SPI		ARD
PSO		SIS
NER		ESS
OBL		ITY
GAL		ONE
FRU		RER
DEL		ATE

LST	TIC	INE	KEN	BST
RIA	VEL	ORE	ITE	IQU

Complete the words in the grid by
filling each space with a group of
three letters from the list.

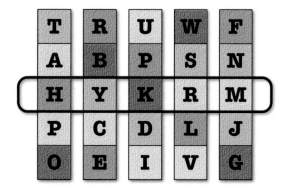

Move the letter strips through the
code slide to find a five-letter word.

EVER
EVER
EVER
EVER
HOUR HOUR HOUR HOUR
HOUR HOUR HOUR HOUR
HOUR HOUR HOUR HOUR
HOUR HOUR HOUR HOUR
HOUR HOUR HOUR HOUR
HOUR HOUR HOUR HOUR

What phrase is represented here?

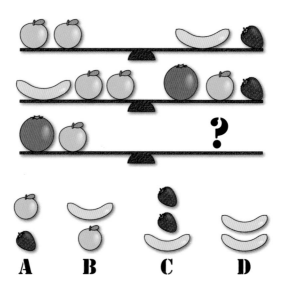

A **B** **C** **D**

Which group of fruit
balances the scale?

a) **D + FUSS = BORDER**

b) **F + MEADOW = INSECT**

c) **T + MINERAL = DAMAGED**

Can you find the words?

Example: c + bone = cot

c + rib = crib

1. "THEN COME AND KISS ME, SWEET AND ..."

2. CATCH —, NOVEL

3. DAYS OF CHRISTMAS

4. LEGS ON A WOODLOUSE

5. VERTEBRAE IN THE HUMAN SPINE

6. NUMBER OF CARDS IN A SUIT

7. BLACKBIRDS BAKED IN A PIE

8. SIDES TO EVERY QUESTION

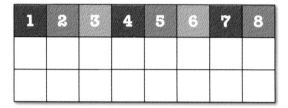

1	2	3	4	5	6	7	8

The answer to each of the clues
on the opposite page is a number.
Place the answers in the
correct square in the top row of
the grid above. Then, using the code
A=26, B=25 etc, place a letter
of the alphabet under each
number to spell out a word.

32

Using two straight lines, can
you divide the clock face
into three sections in which the
numbers total the same?

Can you divide the fishpond into
three sections so that each
section has three striped fish,
two blue fish, two green fish
and one yellow fish?

34

2	3	5	8
3	6	8	9
4	5	7	10
5	8	10	?

Can you fill in the missing number?

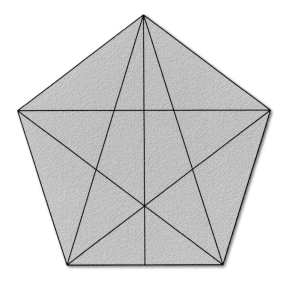

How many triangles
are there in the diagram?

36

31
28
31
30
?

Which number comes next
in this sequence?

Which number should replace
the question mark?

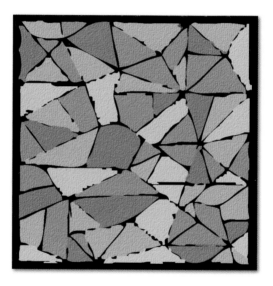

Can you find the hidden star?

Fred is 24 years old and is twice as old as Joe was when Fred was as old as Joe is now.

How old is Joe?

40

a) P + EDGE = STRAIGHTLACED

b) R + FITTING = ABSORBED

c) H + MELODY = LOCKS

Can you find the words?

Example: c + bone = cot

c + rib = crib

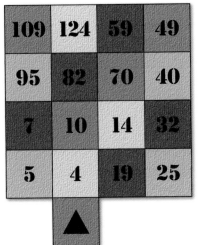

109	124	59	49
95	82	70	40
7	10	14	32
5	4	19	25

Can you trace the correct route
through the maze, starting at
the arrowed square and only
moving one square at a time?

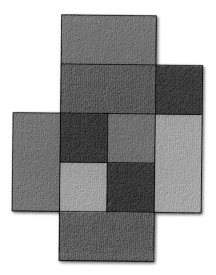

How many squares are there?

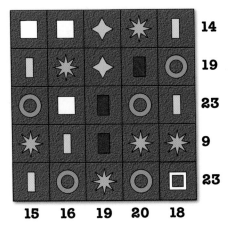

14
19
23
9
23

15 16 19 20 18

Each symbol represents a different figure from 1 to 7. Can you work out which figure each symbol represents?

7
9
9
12
11
15
13
18
15
?

Which number should come next?

45

a) **PARENT OF AN ELVER**

b) **ACHILLES' WEAK SPOT**

c) **USED BY ARTISTS**

D) **FOUND ON THE BEACH**

The computer was malfunctioning.
It gave the answer to each
clue in numbers. How?

46

a) COW. LOW. BOUGH. NOW.

b) IRON. SILVER. LEAD. CARBON.

c) LAKE. STREAM. WATER. OCEAN.

Which is the odd one out?

Which number comes next in the grid?

48

3 digits	4 digits	5 digits
112	1198	52830
274	1996	53341
315	3101	53629
329	3847	
502	3923	**7 digits**
584	3930	8313846
636	4170	8392016
647	4892	
686	5148	
713	5804	
717	6274	
750	~~6591~~	
818	6817	
857	7291	
874	7891	
904	9125	
	9828	
	9960	

Write the listed numbers in
the grid so that they
all fit. We've placed one
number to start you off.

231
462
693
924
?

What number comes next
in this sequence?

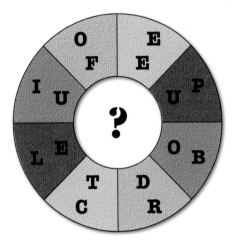

Place a letter in the center of
the circle so that four five-letter
words can be rearranged from each
straight line of letters.

5873	3875	7853	5738
3578	5783	8735	8537
7358	8375	3758	7358
8753	7835	?	3857
7583	3587	5837	8357
5387	5378	8573	3785

Using the figures 3578
and without repeating a used
combination of numbers,
which number should fill the blank?

If ▢ = N and ◲ = U

Can you decipher this message?

53

1. Unblemished and pale with the vertically challenged
2. Gargantuan
3. The virtuous, the morally compromised and the facially disadvantaged
4. Rule of the muscidaes
5. The breeze amidst osiers
6. The womb of interconnectedness
7. The fruits of ire
8. The tome of dense vegetation
9. Fluid from a coleopterous insect
10. Diminutive ladies

Can you work out the book and film titles?

Remove six matches to leave
a) three squares and
b) five squares.

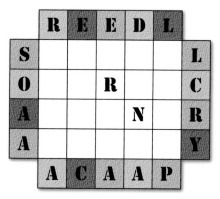

Complete the grid using the 18 letters surrounding it to form four words reading across and five reading down. Each of the surrounding letters must go in the column or row it is placed against.

Can you work out which numbers should go into the spaces in the grid?

57

a) - - - EAR

b) D - - - RITE

c) FRI - - -

d) PREB - - - ARY

What three-letter word will
complete the words above?

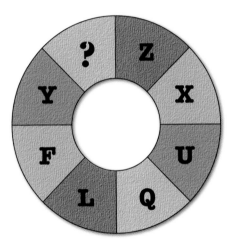

What letter completes the sequence?

59

It is not next to a tree.

It is not next to a plane.

It is not above a mail box.

It is not below a sun.

It is not next to anything red.

It is not next to a blue square.

It is not in a row with a sword.

It is not in a column with a flag.

Using the clues above, can you work out which square, in the grid opposite, the treasure is in?

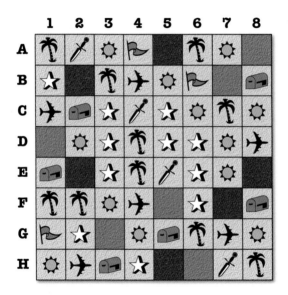

1. RODENT OFTEN KEPT AS A PET

2. SMALL RIVER

3. CLEVER, OR DAPPER

4. DISTANT SUN

5. CREATION OF WORKS OF BEAUTY

6. RIP

7. ANGRY

8. KEEP

9. SURE

Write the solutions to
the clues in their numbered
layers of blocks. Each word is an
anagram of the next layer with one
letter added or taken away.

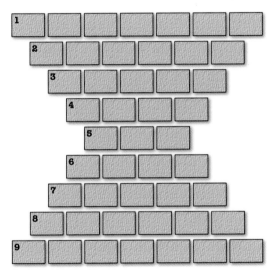

61

There are three sealed caskets,
all incorrectly labeled. One
contains rubies, one emeralds
and one both rubies and emeralds.
The Sheikh tells Scheherazade that
if she can label the caskets
correctly, she can have all the
jewels. She can only open ONE
casket and CANNOT LOOK INSIDE it.
Scheherazade successfully labels
all the caskets. How does she do it?

1344115
1113242115
31131214122115
1321131112111411222115
?

Can you complete the last row?

63

OPEN SECRET

SERIOUSLY FUNNY

BACK OUT

SILENT SCREAM

DIVORCE COURT

PRETTY UGLY

Which pair of words does not fit?

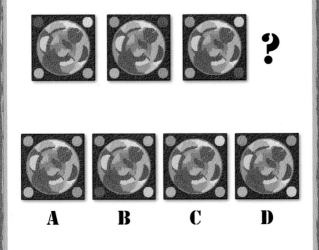

What is the next image in the
screen saver sequence?

65

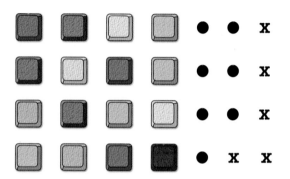

Using the visual clues can you
work out the correct order of
the buttons? A black dot indicates a
correct color in a correct place;
a cross indicates a correct color
in an incorrect position.

PICK		MONEY
POISON		LEAGUE
CREDIT		BOARD
FALSE		CLOCK
QUICK		PIT
WET		CASE
SOAP		HOUSE

The solution to each line is a
word which can come after the first
word and before the second to form
a new word or a two-word phrase.
Enter the solutions in the white
column. Their initial letters will
spell out the name of a painter.

RHYMES WITH	MEANING OF ANAGRAM
Top	Jumps on one leg (hops)
1. Kneel	A vegetable
2. Prize	Lord
3. Spine	Right to keep in lieu of debt
4. Eclair	20 quires
5. Croup	A musical composition
6. Elope	A minute opening
7. Turf	Animal pelts
8. Diet	Three

In the grid on these two pages, the object is to find the word to put in

LINKED WITH	WORD
Keeper	Shop
Haul	
Sun	
Royal	
Night	
Kitchen	
Ladder	
Board	
Squad	

the last column above, using the clues
given. An example has been given.

68

AR   LY
CH   NE
CL   QU
CO   RY
ED   SC
ET   SE
GE

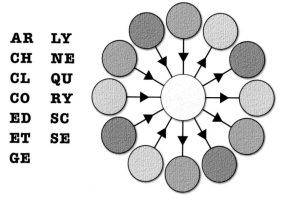

Enter each pair of letters in
a circle so that each line forms a
six-letter word reading in the
direction of the arrows. The two
letters in the center circle will
appear in the middle of each word.

A **B** **C** **D**

Which jigsaw piece does not
fit into the puzzle?

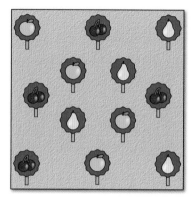

A farmer decided to divide his orchard up between his children in such a way that each child got one apple tree, one pear tree and one cherry tree and an equal amount of land. Using only straight lines how did he do it?

NOV 14 2001

JUNE 31 1889

AUGUST 17 1968

Which is the odd one out?

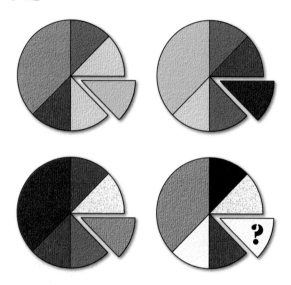

Which color should the slice
with the question mark be?

Find one letter to go in the center of the fan which will turn the letters on each blade, when rearranged, into eight-letter words.

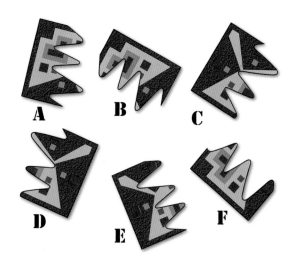

A

B

C

D

E

F

Which two pieces form a square?

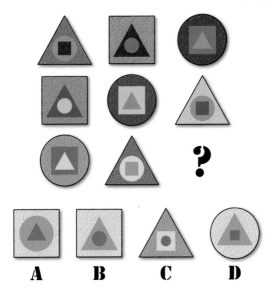

75

A **B** **C** **D**

Which figure completes the sequence?

AM	TI	REND	PATER	QUADRI
AR	UC	ROLE	QUOTA	WARDER
AS	ACE	TIME	RUNNY	ARREARS
AT	ATP	WIMP	TEPEE	EMERGED
BN	ECG	ARRAY	VEILS	FEBRILE
CI	ONE	AWARD	AMERCE	MEIOTIC
CR	RAY	CARNE	CEDING	RUMMAGE
EE	WON	DANES	ESPIER	RUMPERE
EP	ADAM	DIANE	HOOPED	SITUATE
GE	ARCS	EMCEE	LITERA	TODDLER
OD	ELMS	OMBRE	OPENER	VETERAN
PL	NAUT	OTTER	ORCHIL	GENIALLY
PM	ORES	PAPIO	PYEDOG	LETTERED
SR	PROV	ENCYCLOPEDIAS		ITTYBITTY

Can you fit all these into
the grid? Two letters have been
put in to start you off.

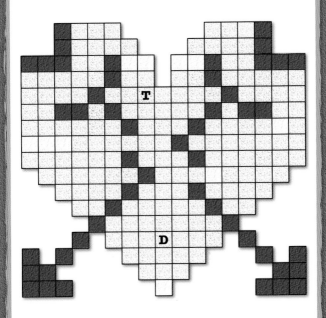

SOLUTIONS

1. He who laughs last, laughs longest.

2.

3. She lives in Antarctica where, during winter, the sun does not rise for six months.

4. RED in the FACE.

5. a) Bib
b) Peep
c) Radar

6. The pink one.
The others, starting from the top, are the colors of the rainbow in correct order: red, orange, yellow, green, blue, indigo, violet.

7. a) Sculpture
b) Watch
c) Antarctica

8. Y.
Hydra, Bayou
Style, Yacht

9. C.

10. Jumping to conclusions.

11. John's birthday is December 31st. His uncle phoned him a day later, on January 1st.

12.

13. Exarchate, Kittiwake, Fenugreek, Wineglass, Tremulous, Slingback, Recipient, Priestess, Crossfire, Animality.

14. a) Weather balloon

b) Song thrush

c) Acid

15. Orange. The first two, mixed together, make the third, four and five will make the next.

16.

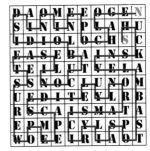

Shucks, Snivel, Lambast, Topsail, Lyricism, Matronly, Yuletide, Escapee, Empower, Russet.

SOLUTIONS

Teasel, Linocut, Tabloid, Disdain, Nominee, Epoch, Halogen.

17. First he takes the antelope and leaves him on the island. Then he returns for the chimp. He takes the chimp to the island and brings the antelope back with him. Then he leaves the antelope behind and takes the lion to the island. Finally he returns with an empty boat and rescues the antelope.

18. 111 = 37 x 3
222 = 37 x 6
333 = 37 x 9

19. Root canal.

20.

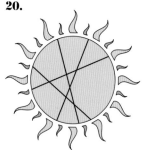

21. Water. The others read the same when held up to a mirror.

22. Roadster, roaster, raster, rater, rate, ate, at, a.

23. 1. Boyd
2. Basil

3. Boris

4. Bertram.

24.

25. Fill the 7-liter bucket and from this fill the 5-liter bucket. Empty the 5-liter bucket and then tip the remaining 2 liters from the 7-liter bucket into the 5-liter bucket. Now fill the 7-liter bucket and you have 9 liters.

26. Kerbstone, Witticism

Theoretic, Spikenard, Psoriasis, Nerveless, Obliquity, Gallstone, Fruiterer, Delineate.

27. PRISM.

28. Forever and a day.

29. D. Strawberry = 1
Apple = 2
Banana = 3
Orange = 4

30. a) dado
b) flea
c) tore

31.

1	2	3	4	5	6	7	8
20	22	12	14	26	13	24	2
G	E	O	M	A	N	C	Y

SOLUTIONS

32.

33.

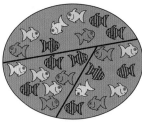

34. 11

35. 53.

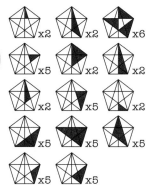

36. 31. Numbers are days in the months of the year.

37. 77.
Numbers in the top half of the circle, starting from the left, are multiplied

by 4, 5, 6, 7, respectively and the answer put in the opposite sector.

38.

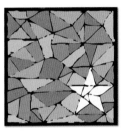

39. Joe is 18. He was 12 when Fred was 18.

40. a) prim
b) rapt
c) hair

41. 4, 5, 7, 10, 14, 19, 25, 32, 40, 49, 59, 70, 82, 95, 109, 124.
Number progression is +1, +2, +3 and so on.

42. 12.

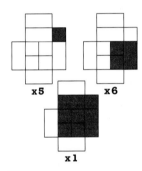

43.

☀ = 1	▯ = 2	☐ = 3
■ = 4	◆ = 5	▢ = 6
◯ = 7		

SOLUTIONS

44. 21. There are two alternate series. The first increases by two each time, the second by 3.

45. Turn the page upside down and the numbers look like letters.
a) 733
b) 7334
c) 5710
d) 77345

46. a) Low. The others rhyme.
b) Carbon. The others are metals.
c) Water. The others are composed of water.

47. 28. In each row, halve the first number to get the second, multiply that by the third to get the fourth.

48.

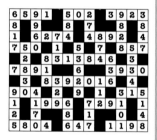

6	5	9	1		5	0	2		3	9	2	3
8		9			8		7			8		8
1		6	2	7	4		4	8	9	2		4
7	5	0		1		5		7		8	5	7
	2		8	3	1	3	8	4	6		3	
7	8	9	1			6			3	9	3	0
	3		8	3	9	2	0	1	6		4	
9	0	4		2		9		1		3	1	5
1		1	9	9	6		7	2	9	1		1
2		7		8		1		0		4
5	8	0	4		6	4	7		1	1	9	8

49. 1155
The numbers increase by 231 each time.

50. Fjord, Julep, Bijou, Eject.

51. 7385.

52. It will be pleasant to recollect this some day.

A	B	C	J	K	L	S	T	U
· D	E	F	: M	N	O	: V	W	X
G	H	I	P	Q	R	Y	Z	

53. 1. Snow White and the Seven Dwarfs

2. Titanic

3. The Good, the Bad and the Ugly

4. Lord of the Flies

5. The Wind in the Willows

6. The Matrix

7. The Grapes of Wrath

8. The Jungle Book

9. Beetlejuice

10. Little Women

54.

a)

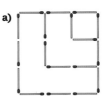

b)

55. Reading across:
Scalp, Coral,
Arena, Ready.

Reading down:
Scar, Core, Area,
Land, Play.

SOLUTIONS

56.

3	5	8	2	1	4
5	6	3	0	7	2
8	3	4	5	6	9
2	0	5	1	3	6
1	7	6	3	4	5
4	2	9	6	5	8

57. END. Endear, dendrite friend, prebendary.

58. Q. Starting at Z and working through the alphabet in reverse, there is one extra letter between the letters each time.

59. D3

60. 1 Hamster, 2 Stream, 3 Smart, 4 Star, 5 Art, 6 Tear, 7 Irate, 8 Retain, 9 Certain.

61. She opens the casket labeled 'Rubies and Emeralds', took out one jewel, looked at it and put it back. She then put the correct label on that casket, moved the other label to the now unlabeled casket and then put the 'Rubies and Emeralds' label on the final casket.

62.

1 1 1 3 1 2 2 1 1 3 3 1 1
2 3 1 1 4 2 1 3 2 2 1 1 5

Each row describes the preceding row eg, second

row reads: one 'one', one 'three', two 'fours', two 'ones', one 'five'.

63. Back out. The others are oxymorons.

64. B. The red outer circle moves round one place each time.

65.

66. Pocket, Ivy, Card, Alarm, Sand, Suit, Opera. Painter: Picasso.

67. 1. Keel (anag: leek)
2. Rise (anag: Sire)
3. Line (anag: Lien)

4. Mare (anag: Ream)
5. Soup (anag: Opus)
6. Rope (anag: Pore)
7. Surf (anag: Furs)
8. Riot (anag: Trio)

68. Charge, Claret, Coarse, Nearly, Quarry, Scared.

69. D.

70.

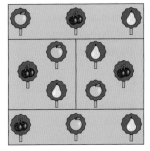